'Brave French will you not surrender?' Cambronne answered, *'Merde!'*

VICTOR HUGO
Born 1802, Besançon, France
Died 1885, Paris, France

Les Misérables was first published in 1862.
This translation was first published in 1976.

VICTOR HUGO IN PENGUIN CLASSICS
Les Misérables
Notre-Dame de Paris

VICTOR HUGO

Waterloo

Translated by
Norman Denny

PENGUIN BOOKS

PENGUIN CLASSICS

UK | USA | Canada | Ireland | Australia
India | New Zealand | South Africa

Penguin Classics is part of the Penguin Random House group of companies
whose addresses can be found at global.penguinrandomhouse.com.

This selection first published in Penguin Classics 2016
001

Translation copyright © Norman Denny, 1976

The moral right of the translator has been asserted

Set in 9/12.4 pt Baskerville 10 Pro
Typeset by Jouve (UK), Milton Keynes
Printed in Great Britain by Clays Ltd, St Ives plc

A CIP catalogue record for this book is available from the British Library

ISBN: 978-0-241-25182-9

www.greenpenguin.co.uk

18 June 1815

Had it not rained in the night of 17–18 June 1815, the future of Europe would have been different. A few drops of water, more or less, were what decided Napoleon's fate. Providence needed only a downpour of rain to make Waterloo the retort to Austerlitz. An unseasonably clouded sky sufficed to bring about the collapse of a world.

The Battle of Waterloo could not start until eleven-thirty because the ground was too wet. It had to dry out a little before the artillery could manoeuvre. And it was this that enabled Blücher to arrive in time.

Napoleon was an artillery officer and never forgot it. At the heart of this prodigious commander was the man who had reported to the Directory after the Battle of Aboukir, 'Some of our shot killed six men.' All his battle-plans were designed to suit the heavy armament. To bring the artillery to bear on the critical point, this to him was the key to victory. He treated the enemy general's strategy as though he were attacking a fortress, and he breached it. He pounded the weak points with grape-shot, and shaped and resolved battles with cannon-fire. His was a marksman's genius. To beat in the squares, pulverize the regiments, break the lines, maul and scatter the mass, this was the secret – ceaseless hammering – and it was done by the use of cannon. This formidable procedure, applied with genius, rendered him invincible for fifteen years, a dark master of the pugilism of war.

He relied more than ever on artillery in that June of 1815 because he had the advantage of numbers. Wellington had only 159 guns; Napoleon had 240.

Had the ground been dry, so that the artillery could move, the battle would have begun at six in the morning; it would have been over and done with by two, three hours before the Prussians could turn the scales.

How much of the blame for his defeat is to be attributed to Napoleon? Is the navigator necessarily responsible for the shipwreck?

Was Napoleon's undeniable physical decline at this stage accompanied by a weakening of his faculties? Had twenty years of warfare worn the blade as well as the scabbard, the soul as well as the body? Was the veteran becoming sadly manifest in the commander? In a word, was his genius fading, as many reputable historians believe, and was he frenziedly seeking to hide the fact from himself? Was he beginning to waver under chance setbacks, or – a grave weakness in a general – was he becoming careless of danger? Is there a point in the lives of men who may be termed the giants of action when their vision becomes clouded? Age is no threat to the great men of the mind. With the Dantes and the Michelangelos, to grow older is to grow: is it to shrink, in the case of the Hannibals and the Bonapartes? Had Napoleon lost his flair for victory? Was he no longer able to foresee the pitfall, to detect the trap, to discern the crumbling edge of the abyss; had he lost his instinct for averting disaster? He who had travelled all the roads to triumph, pointing the way with a lordly finger from his fiery chariot, was he now so locked in obsession as to lead his tumultuous following of legions over the precipice? Had he, at the age of forty-six, gone finally mad? Had this titanic coachman of destiny become no more than a breakneck driver?

We do not believe this.

His plan of battle, it is generally acknowledged, was masterly. It was to drive straight for the gap between the Allied forces and divide them in two, pushing the British towards Hal and the Prussians towards Tongres, and making of Wellington and Blücher two separate segments. Mont-Saint-Jean was to be carried and Brussels seized, the Germans flung back to the Rhine and the English into the sea. All this Napoleon intended to achieve by means of this battle; after which he would review the position.

It goes without saying that we do not claim to be writing a history of Waterloo. A critical moment in our tale is linked with the battle, but its history is not our concern. This has, in any case, been admirably recounted by Napoleon himself, from one point of view, and from other aspects by a galaxy of historians.

For our part, we leave to the experts their task, being ourselves no more than a remote observer, a traveller across the plain, scrutinizing that earth sodden with human blood and perhaps mistaking the appearance for the reality. We are not competent to deal in scholarly terms with a mass of facts in which, no doubt, there is an element of illusion, nor do we possess the military or strategic competence which would enable us to assess them professionally. It appears to us that a series of hazards dictated the course of events at Waterloo; and as for Destiny, that mysterious culprit, we judge it like those simple-minded judges, the common people.

'A'

To form a clear idea of the Battle of Waterloo we have only to draw a capital A. The left leg of the A is the road from Nivelles, the right leg is the road from Genappe, and the cross is the sunken lane from Ohain to Braine-l'Alleud. The point of the A is Mont-Saint-Jean, where Wellington was. The foot of the left leg is Hougomont, where Reille and Jerome Bonaparte were, and the foot of the right leg is La-Belle-Alliance, Napoleon's headquarters. A little below the point where the cross of the A meets the right leg is La-Haie-Sainte; and the middle of the cross is the precise spot where the battle was decided. That is where the lion has been placed, and unwitting symbol of the supreme heroism of the Imperial Guard. The triangle formed by the upper part of the A is the plateau of Mont-Saint-Jean, the struggle for which was the essence of the battle.

The wings of the two armies extended to right and left of the roads from Genappe and Nivelles, d'Erlon facing Picton and Reille facing Hill. Beyond the apex of the A and the plateau of Mont-Saint-Jean lies the forest of Soignes.

As for the plain itself, imagine a wide rolling landscape, each successive fold dominating its predecessor, the whole rising to Mont-Saint-Jean and ending in the forest.

Two hostile armies on a field of battle are like two

wrestlers, bodies interlocked, each seeking to throw the other. Everything is turned to account, the thicket becomes a strong-point, the angle of a wall a buttress. Lacking any kind of shelter, a regiment may give ground; but a dip in the plain, an irregularity in the terrain, a convenient cross-road, a wood or a ravine, any of these may suffice to stay the feet of the colossus known as an army and prevent its retreat. He who abandons the field is beaten. Hence the necessity for the responsible commander to examine every feature of the countryside.

Both generals had carefully studied the plain of Mont-Saint-Jean, now called the plain of Waterloo. Wellington, with commendable foresight, had ridden over it the previous year, seeing in it a possible setting for a major battle. In the event he was the more favourably situated, the British army being on higher ground than the French.

To attempt a picture of Napoleon on that morning of 18 June, seated on his horse on the height of Rossomme with his field-glass in his hand, is scarcely necessary. Everyone is familiar with it, the calm profile under the small cocked hat of the College of Brienne, the green tunic with white facings, the grey top-coat hiding the epaulettes, the glimpse of red sash under the waistcoat, the leather breeches, the white horse with its cloth of purple velvet embroidered at the corners with a crowned N and an eagle, the cavalry boots worn over silk stockings, the silver spurs, the Marengo sword – this picture of the last Caesar lives in the memory of all men, acclaimed by some and reviled by others.

The figure has long been fully illumined, having emerged from the kind of legendary fog that emanates from most great men, and for a time hides the truth about them. Today history and broad daylight are one.

The daylight of history is merciless; it has the strange and magical quality that, although it is composed of light, and precisely because of this, it casts shadows where once only brilliance was to be seen, making of one man two images, each opposed to the other, so that the darkness of the despot counteracts the majesty of the leader. Thus the world arrives at a more balanced judgement. Babylon ravished diminishes Alexander, Rome in chains diminishes Caesar, Jerusalem sacked diminishes Titus. Tyranny follows the tyrant. It is grievous for a man to leave behind him a shadow in his own shape.

The fog of war

Everybody knows about the early stage of the battle, the tentative uncertain opening, dangerous for both armies but more so for the English than for the French.

It had rained all night and the ground was sodden with the downpour. Water lay in pools, in some places coming up to the axles of the ammunition-limbers and covering the lower harness with mud. If the crops of wheat and rye crushed under the wheels of the mass of vehicles had not partly filled in the ruts, all movement, particularly in the small valleys round Papelotte, would have been impossible.

The action was late in beginning. Napoleon, as we have said, was accustomed to keep the artillery under his direct command, using it like a pistol to be aimed at particular points in the battle, and for this it was necessary for the sun to come out and dry the ground so that the batteries could move at a gallop as required. But the sun did not shine. This was not Austerlitz. When the first gun was fired General Colville looked at his watch and noted that the time was eleven thirty-five.

The battle began with a furious assault – more furious, perhaps, than the Emperor intended – by the French left wing on Hougomont. At the same time Napoleon attacked in the centre, flinging Quiot's brigade against La-Haie-Sainte, while Ney thrust with the French right wing against the English left, occupying Papelotte.

The attack on Hougomont was partly a feint intended to induce Wellington to concentrate on that flank. The plan would have succeeded had not the four companies of English Guards and a detachment of Belgians from Perponcher's division clung so stubbornly to the position that Wellington needed only to reinforce them with four more companies of Guards and a battalion of Brunswickers.

The intention of the right-wing attack on Papelotte was to break the English left, cut the road to Brussels, thus barring the way to the Prussians, carry Mont-Saint-Jean, and force Wellington to fall back, first on Hougomont, then on Braine-l'Alleud and then on Hal. It was a clear-cut plan which largely succeeded. Papelotte and La-Haie-Sainte were both taken.

A detail may here be noted. The British infantry, especially Kempt's brigade, included a great many raw recruits. These young soldiers bore themselves gallantly against our own redoubtable infantry and despite their inexperience came out of the affair with honour. In particular they did excellent service as sharp-shooters. The sharp-shooter, being to some extent on his own, may be said to be his own commander. Novices though they were, these recruits had dash and showed themselves to possess something of the French capacity for improvisation. This did not altogether please Wellington.

After the fall of La-Haie-Sainte the battle hung in the balance. This middle phase, from midday until four o'clock, is indistinctly visible, shrouded in the fog of war. We have a glimpse of huge turmoil, a kaleidoscopic picture of outmoded military trappings, busbies, sabre-belts, crossed shoulder-straps, ammunition pouches, hussars' dolmans, wrinkled red riding-boots, heavy fringed shakos, the black tunics of Brunswick mingled with the scarlet of England, English soldiers with white-padded epaulettes, Hanoverian light horse in their narrow, red-plumed helmets, bare-kneed Scots in plaid and kilts, the white gaiters of our own grenadiers – isolated incidents rather than battle-lines, more suited to a painter such as Salvator Rosa than to an artillery commander such as Gribeauval.

There is an element of tempestuous convulsion in every battle – *quid obscurum, quid divinum* – and every historian, peering into the mêlée, can find what he looks for. Whatever the calculations of the generals, the clash of armed masses has unpredictable repercussions; each commander's plan shapes and distorts that of the other. One sector of the battlefield swallows up more combatants than another, just as water drains away more or less rapidly according to the nature of the soil. More men have to be sent to a particular point than was originally intended, the line writhes and wavers like a thread blowing in the wind. There is no logic in the flow of blood; the army fronts are like waves on the seashore, advancing and retreating regiments forming bays and headlands, impermanent as a shifting sand. Where there was infantry, artillery appears; artillery is replaced by cavalry; battalions are like puffs of smoke. At a given place there was a given object: look for it again and it is gone. The light shifts, the dark patches advance and retreat, a grave-yard wind blows, driving and scattering the tragic multitude of men. All is movement and oscillation. The immobility of a mathematical plan or diagram may present a moment but never a day. To depict a battle we need a painter with chaos in his brush. Rembrandt is better than Van der Meulen; he who was accurate at noon is a liar by three o'clock. Geometry is misleading; only the tempest is true. And there comes a stage in every battle when it degenerates into hand-to-hand combat, dissolves in fragments, innumerable separate episodes concerning which Napoleon himself said that they belong more to regimental records than to the history of an army. Thus the historian has a right to summarize. He can do no more than grasp the broad outline. No narrator, be he never so conscientious, can fix the exact shape of that ugly cloud that is called a battle.

This, which is true of all great clashes between armies, applies particularly to Waterloo. Nevertheless there came a point, during the afternoon, when the shape of the battle was defined.

Four o'clock in the afternoon

At about four o'clock Wellington's army was in serious trouble. The Prince of Orange was in command of the centre, with Hill commanding the right wing and Picton the left. The Prince, gallant and despairing, was calling upon his lowlanders, the men of Nassau and Brunswick, to stand fast. Hill, greatly weakened, was falling back upon Wellington and the reserve. Picton was dead, killed by a ball through the head at the moment when the colours of the French 105th regiment of the line had been captured by the English. For Wellington there were two critical points, Hougomont and La-Haie-Sainte. Hougomont was still holding out, but in flames. La-Haie-Sainte had fallen. Three thousand men had died in that farm. Of the German battalion which was among its defenders only five officers and forty-two men survived. The cavalry force of 1200 horses had lost half its strength, the Scots Greys and Ponsonby's heavy dragoons having been overwhelmed by Bro's lancers and Travers's cuirassiers. Most of its officers had fallen. Two infantry divisions, the fifth and sixth, had been virtually destroyed.

With Hougomont breached and La-Haie-Sainte captured, only one strong-point remained, the centre. This was still holding, and Wellington reinforced it, bringing in Hill, who was at Merbe-Braine, and Chassé, who was at Braine-l'Alleud.

The English centre, slightly concave, very dense and compact, was in a strong position. It occupied the plateau of

Mont-Saint-Jean, with the village behind it and a steep slope in front. At its back was a stone mansion, part of the state-owned domain of Nivelles, standing at the road-intersection, a sixteenth-century building of such solid construction that musket-fire ricocheted off it. The trees and thickets bordering the plateau had been pruned to create embrasures and loop-holes behind which the guns waited in ambush, and this work of concealment, an entirely legitimate stratagem of war, had been so skilfully carried out that Haxo, who had been sent by Napoleon to reconnoitre the enemy batteries, saw nothing and reported that there were no defence works other than the barricades on the road to Nivelles and Genappe. It was the time of year when the crops are in full growth, and a battalion of Kempt's brigade, armed with carbines, lay hidden in the standing corn.

In short, the Anglo-Dutch centre was well placed. What endangered its position was the forest of Soignes, a wide extent of woodland in its rear containing the marshes of Groenandel and Boitsfort. An army could not hope to carry out an orderly withdrawal over this rough terrain, where its units were bound to become separated and the artillery likely to be bogged down in the swamps. Many of the officers maintained – although it must be said that others disagreed with them – that retreat would become a rout.

Wellington reinforced the centre with one of Chassé's brigades, brought in from the right wing, one of Wincke's brigades, from the left, and Clinton's division. In support of his British contingent, consisting of Halkett's command,

Mitchell's brigade, and Maitland's Guards, he brought in the Brunswick infantry, the Nassau contingent, Kielmansegge's Hanoverians, and Ompteda's Germans. Thus he had twenty-six battalions under his direct command. As Charras has said, 'The right wing was folded back behind the centre.' A very powerful battery occupied a fortified position on the site of what is now known as 'the Waterloo Museum'. In addition, concealed in a fold in the ground, Wellington had Somerset's Dragoon Guards, the other half of the justly renowned English cavalry. Ponsonby had been wiped out (he himself had been killed), but Somerset remained.

The battery, which might almost have been termed a redoubt if the work had been finished, was drawn up behind a low garden wall, hastily reinforced with sandbags, with a broad, open slope in front of it. There had been no time to complete its defence works.

Wellington, worried but impassive, had remained throughout the day seated on his horse in the same place, a little in front of the ancient mill of Mont-Saint-Jean, which still exists, and in the shade of an elm-tree which an Englishman, a vandal enthusiast, subsequently bought for 200 francs, cut down and took away. Wellington's bearing was one of icy heroism. The bullets whistled past him. Gordon, one of his aides, was killed at his side. Lord Hill demanded of him after a shell-burst, 'What are your orders, my lord, if you are killed?' . . . 'Do what I'm doing,' Wellington replied, and he said tersely to Clinton, 'Hang on to the last man.' When things were clearly going badly he cried to the men of Talavera, Vitoria, and Salamanca, 'Don't yield an inch. Think of England!'

But at about four o'clock the English line wavered. There was suddenly nothing to be seen on the high ground of the plateau but the guns and gun-crews. The infantry regiments, unable to withstand the hail of French cannon and musketry fire, had taken refuge in the depression which the farm lane of Mont-Saint-Jean still crosses. There was a general movement of withdrawal. Wellington's battle-line was crumbling. 'It's the beginning of the retreat!' Napoleon cried.

Napoleon is well-pleased

Although he was a sick man and troubled by a local ailment which made riding uncomfortable, the Emperor had never been in higher spirits than on that day. Since the morning his inscrutable countenance had worn a smile. The man of marble, the profound visionary, was blindly radiant on that day of 18 June 1815; the frowning commander of Austerlitz was happy at Waterloo. Thus does Destiny deceive us; our joys are shadows, the last laugh is God's.

'*Ridet Caesar, Pompieus flebit* – if Caesar laughs Pompey will weep,' said the men of the Fulminatrix legion. Pompey did not weep on this occasion, but it is certain that Caesar laughed.

It had seemed to Napoleon, since he and Bertrand had ridden after midnight through thunder and rain to the heights near Rossomme, thence to survey the line of English camp-fires lighting the horizon from Frischemont to Braine-l'Alleud, that the appointment with destiny fixed by him for the coming day on the field of Waterloo had been rightly determined. He had reined in his horse and sat for some time motionless gazing at the lightning and listening to the thunder; and, fatalist that he was, he had been heard to mutter the cryptic words, 'We are of one mind.' But Napoleon was mistaken. Destiny and he were no longer of one mind.

He had spent no time at all in sleep, every minute of that night bringing a new cause for satisfaction. He had made the round of the picket-lines, pausing here and there to talk to the men. At half past two, near the wood of Hougomont, he heard the sound of a marching column and for a moment had thought that Wellington was already withdrawing. 'It's the English rear-guard getting ready to clear out,' he said to Bertrand. 'I shall capture the six thousand English who have just landed at Ostend.' He was talking expansively, with the ardour he had shown when they disembarked in the Golfe Juan on 1 March, and pointing to a cheering peasant he exclaimed, 'There you are, Bertrand – a reinforcement already!' On this night of 17 June he mocked Wellington, saying, 'That Englishman needs a lesson.' The rain fell more heavily and there was a crash of thunder as he spoke.

At three-thirty that morning he lost one of his illusions. The officers sent out to reconnoitre reported that there was no movement in the enemy lines. Nothing was stirring, no camp-fires had been extinguished. Wellington's army was asleep; a profound silence reigned on earth while the skies resounded. At four o'clock a peasant was brought in who had acted as guide to an English cavalry column, probably Vivian's brigade, on its way to take up its position in the village of Ohain, on the extreme left. At five o'clock two Belgian deserters were brought in who said that the English army was awaiting battle. 'So much the better!' cried Napoleon. 'I'd sooner bowl them over than drive them back.'

At daybreak he dismounted on to the mud of the grass verge at the turn of the road from Plancenoit. He sent to Rossomme farm for a kitchen table and chair, and there seated himself, with a truss of straw for a footstool and a map of the battlefield spread out in front of him, saying to Soult, *'Joli échiquier'* – 'a nice chess-board!'

Owing to the rain and the state of the roads the commissariat convoys had not arrived; the soldiers had had little sleep and were wet and hungry; but this did not deter Napoleon from exclaiming blithely to Ney, 'Our chances are ninety in a hundred.' Breakfast was served to the Emperor at eight o'clock and he invited a number of his generals to join him. Over breakfast they discussed the fact that two nights previously Wellington had attended the Duchess of Richmond's ball in Brussels, and Soult, that rough warrior with the face of an archbishop, said, 'The real ball will be held today.' Napoleon laughed at Ney, who said, 'Wellington won't be such a fool as to wait for your majesty.' This was the kind of talk he enjoyed. 'He loved to tease,' said Fleury de Chaboulon. 'A lively humour was at the root of his nature,' said Gourgand; and Benjamin Constant said, 'He was full of jokes, more crude than witty.' This aspect of the great man deserves to be stressed. It was he who called his grenadiers 'grognards' and pinched their ears or tweaked their moustaches – 'He was always up to some game with us,' one of them said. During the mysterious return from Elba to France, when the French brig-of-war *Zephir* closed with the brig *Inconstant*, in which Napoleon was concealed, and asked for news of him, Napoleon himself, wearing the bee-embroidered hat with a white-and-purple cockade which he had devised in Elba, snatched up the speaking-trumpet and shouted, laughing: 'The Emperor is in excellent health.' The man who can laugh in this fashion feels himself to be in harmony with events. Napoleon had several bursts of laughter during that Waterloo breakfast. When the meal was over he was silent for a quarter of an hour; then two generals seated themselves on a truss of straw with writing-pads on their knee and he dictated the order of battle.

At nine o'clock, when the French army moved off in five columns, divisions in double lines, artillery between the brigades, bands at the head filling the air with the roll of drums and the clamour of trumpets, a powerful, vast, and joyous sea of helmets, sabres, and bayonets extended to the horizon, the Emperor was so moved that he twice cried: 'Magnificent! Magnificent!'

Incredible as it may seem, in the period between nine and ten-thirty the whole army took up its positions, being arrayed in six lines forming, in the Emperor's phrase, 'a pattern of six Vs'. In the profound lull preceding the storm, while he watched the deployment of the three batteries of twelve-centimetre guns detached from the three corps of Erlon, Reille, and Lobau with orders to open the attack by bombarding Mont-Saint-Jean at the intersection of the Nivelles and Genappe roads, the Emperor clapped Haxo on the shoulder, saying, 'Two dozen very pretty girls, General.'

Confident of the outcome, he had a smile of encouragement for the company of sappers from the First Corps, detailed to dig themselves in on Mont-Saint-Jean directly the village was taken. Only one momentary shadow marred the serenity of his mood. Over to his left, in the place where there is today a vast graveyard, he saw the Scots Greys drawn up on their splendid horses, and the sight drew from him an expression of regret – 'It's a pity,' he said.

Then he mounted his own horse and rode to a point a little in front of Rossomme. This narrow strip of grass to the right of the road from Genappe to Brussels was his second observation-post during the battle. (The third, which he went to at seven in the evening, was between La-Belle-Alliance and La-Haie-Sainte.) It is a terribly exposed place, a high, flat-topped mound which still exists, behind which the Imperial Guard was massed in a small depression in the plain. Bullets ricocheted up from the road surface, and as at Brienne the air above his head was filled with the whistle of grape-shot and musketry. The twisted remnants of shot and shell, rusted sabre-blades, and the like were later retrieved from almost the spot where his horse stood, and a few years ago a shell was dug up there with a damaged fuse and its explosive charge intact. It was here that the Emperor said to his guide, Lacoste, a hostile and terrified peasant, roped to the saddle of a hussar, who ducked at every salvo and tried to hide behind the horses, 'Idiot! You ought to be ashamed. Do you want to be shot in the back?' The writer of these lines, digging in the dusty earth of that hillock, himself found the neck of an exploded bomb eaten with the rust of forty-six years, and fragments of metal that broke like twigs in his hands.

The rolling countryside is no longer what it was on that

June day when Napoleon and Wellington met. It has been disfigured for its own glorification, robbed of its natural contours to make a funeral monument, so that history, put out of countenance, can no longer recognize herself. Returning to Waterloo two years later, Wellington exclaimed: 'They have changed my battlefield!' Where the great pyramid of earth surmounted by a lion now stands there was a ridge with a negotiable slope on the side of the Nivelles road but what was almost an escarpment on the side of the Genappe road. Its height can be measured by the height of the two funeral mounds flanking the road from Genappe to Brussels, the one on the left the English memorial and that on the right the German. There is no French memorial. For France the whole plain is a graveyard. Thanks to the many thousand cartloads of earth which have made it into a pyramid 150 feet high and half a mile in circumference, the plateau of Mont-Saint-Jean is now accessible by a gentle incline; but on the day of the battle the approaches were much steeper, particularly on the side of La-Haie-Sainte – so much so that the English guns could not see the farm in the depths of the valley, the centre of the struggle. Moreover the heavy rainfall had ploughed gulleys in the steep slopes, adding mud to the difficulties of the ascent.

Along the crest of the ridge there ran a sort of trench, invisible to the observer at a distance, and this must be described.

Braine-l'Alleud and Ohain are Belgian villages about four miles apart, hidden from one another by the contours of the land and linked by a road that runs like a furrow through the rolling countryside, sometimes following the contours and sometimes buried between hills, so that at many points it is a ravine. In 1815, as now, the road crosses the plateau of Mont-Saint-Jean between the Genappe and Nivelles highways; but whereas it is now level with the surrounding land, it was then a sunken lane. Its two embankments have been removed to make the funeral mound. The greater part of the road was and still is embanked, sometimes to a depth of a dozen feet, with steep, overhanging sides which were liable to crumble under heavy rain. There were accidents. The road was so narrow at the approach to Braine-l'Alleud that in February 1637 a certain Monsieur Bernard Debrye, a Brussels merchant, was run over and killed by a farm-cart – a fact recorded by the stone cross standing near the cemetery. And it was so deep on the Mont-Saint-Jean plateau that a peasant named Mathieu Nicaise was killed by a landslide in 1783; but the cross commemorating this event vanished in the clearance, and nothing of it now remains but its overturned pedestal on the grassy slope to the left of the lane running from La-Haie-Sainte to the Mont-Saint-Jean farm.

On the day of the battle nothing gave warning of this sunken lane flanking the ridge of Mont-Saint-Jean; a deep trench running along the escarpment, a hidden furrow in the earth, invisible and therefore terrible.

The Emperor questions the guide, Lacoste

So on that morning of Waterloo Napoleon was well content, and with reason. His plan of battle, as we have said, was admirable.

Nor did the many vicissitudes of the day dismay him: the holding of Hougomont, the stubborn resistance of La-Haie-Sainte; the death of Bauduin and wounding of Foy; the unexpected wall against which Soye's brigade was broken; the fatal negligence of Guilleminot, who had neither grenades nor powder bags; the bogging down of the batteries; the fifteen unescorted guns overturned by Uxbridge in a sunken lane; the relative ineffectiveness of explosives falling in the sodden earth of the English lines, so that grape-shot wasted itself in a shower of mud; Piré's failure at Braine-l'Alleud and the virtual wiping out of fifteen cavalry squadrons; the English right little shaken, and the left weakly assailed; Ney's strange blunder in advancing the four divisions of the First Corps *en masse* instead of in echelon, twenty-seven lines of two hundred men exposed to cannon-shot and rapid musket-fire, so that their attack was thrown into disorder, the supporting batteries on the flank uncovered, Bourgeois, Donzelot, and Durutte threatened and Quiot repulsed; Lieutenant Vieux, that Herculean product of the École Polytechnique, wounded at the moment when he was breaking down the gate of La-Haie-Sainte with an axe under the plunging fire from the English fortifications barring the turn in the road from Genappe to Brussels; Marcoquet's division caught between infantry and cavalry, mown down at point-blank range in a cornfield by Best and Pack, sabred by Ponsonby, and its battery of seven guns spiked; the Prince of Saxe-Weimar standing his ground against the Comte d'Erlon, Frischemont, and Smohain; the colours of the 105th and 45th line regiments captured; the Prussian Black Hussar captured by scouts of the flying column of *chasseurs* scouring the countryside between Wavre and Planchenoit, and the disturbing things this prisoner told them; Grouchy's late arrival; the fifteen hundred men killed in less than an hour in the orchard of Hougomont, and the eighteen hundred killed at La-Haie-Sainte in an even shorter time – all these stormy events, passing in the fog of battle beneath Napoleon's gaze, seemed scarcely to trouble him or cloud his aspect of imperial certainty. He was accustomed to see war as a whole, never casting up the columns of profit and loss. The figures mattered little to him provided they added up to the right total, which was victory. Early setbacks did not shake him, since he believed himself to be master of the conclusion. He could afford to wait; he was beyond question the equal of Destiny, to whom he seemed to say, 'You would not dare.'

A creature of light and dark, Napoleon believed himself to be protected in good and tolerated in evil. He had, or thought he had, a connivance on his side, one may almost say a complicity in the ordering of events akin to the invulnerability of the antique gods. Yet, with Beresina, Leipzig, and Fontainebleau behind him, he might well have had his doubts about Waterloo – as though a mysterious frown had appeared in the depths of the sky.

But when Wellington recoiled, Napoleon was thrilled. He watched the plateau of Mont-Saint-Jean being rapidly evacuated and the English battle-front disappear. It rallied but kept under cover. The Emperor rose in his stirrups with the light of victory in his eyes. He saw Wellington driven into the forest of Soignes and there destroyed, the final crushing of England by France; Crécy, Poitiers, Malplaquet, and Ramillies revenged. The man of Marengo would exact payment for Agincourt.

Contemplating this fateful prospect, he swept the field of battle for the last time with his glass. His Guard, drawn up with grounded arms on the lower slope behind him, watched him with an almost religious awe. He was intently studying the details of the terrain: slopes and ridges, the odd clump of trees, the barley-field, the footpath, down to the last blade of grass. In particular he examined the barriers of tree-trunks erected by the English across the two highways – the one on the Genappe road overlooking La-Haie-Sainte and armed with two guns which were the only pieces of English artillery bearing on the deepest sector of the battlefield, and the one on the road to Nivelles, behind which gleamed the Dutch bayonets of Chassé's brigade. Close by the latter stood the old, white-washed Chapel of St Nicholas, on a bend in the lane running to Braine-l'Alleud. Napoleon bent down and put a question to the guide, Lacoste, who answered with a shake of his head – probably an act of deliberate treachery.

Then the Emperor straightened up in the saddle and for a moment sat pondering. Wellington had begun to withdraw: all that remained was to turn withdrawal into rout.

He turned abruptly and ordered a dispatch-rider to ride post-haste to Paris with the news that the battle was won.*

He was the genius who commands thunder, and he had his thunderbolt. He ordered the cuirassiers under Milhaud to take the plateau of Mont-Saint-Jean.

The unexpected

There were three thousand five hundred of them, extending over a front of about a mile; twenty-six squadrons of big men on enormous horses. Behind them, in support, were Lefebvre-Desnouettes's division, a picked company of gendarmes, and the contingents of the *chasseurs* and lancers of the Guard. They wore plumeless helmets and metal breastplates and carried cavalry muskets and long sabres. The whole army had watched in admiration when they moved into position at nine o'clock that morning, the dense column with one artillery battery on its flank and another at its centre, deploying in two ranks between the Genappe road and Frischemont to constitute the powerful and shrewdly placed second line which, with Kellermann's cuirassiers on its left wing and Milhaud's on its right, had so to speak two wings of iron.

The Emperor's aide-de-camp, Bertrand, brought them the order. Ney drew his sword and placed himself at the head of the squadrons as they went into action.

---

* This has been questioned. It seems that Grouchy may have misread Napoleon's dispatch.

It was an awe-inspiring sight.

The great force of cavalry, sabres raised and standards fluttering, formed up in columns by divisions, moved as one man down the slope of the Belle-Alliance hill, vanished into the smoke of that fearsome valley where so many men had already fallen, emerged on the other side still in compact, orderly ranks and rode at a canter through a hail of fire up the muddy slope of the Mont-Saint-Jean plateau. They rode steadily, menacingly, imperturbably, the thunder of their horses resounding in the intervals of musket and cannon-fire. Being two divisions they were in two columns, Wathier's division on the right, Delord's on the left.

At a distance they resembled prodigious snakes of steel writhing across the battlefield and up towards the plateau. Nothing like it had been seen since the taking of the great Moskowa redoubt by the heavy cavalry. Murat was absent, but Ney was there. The great mass seemed to have become a monster with a single soul. The separate squadrons rose and fell like the rings of a serpent, disclosing gaps as now and then they became visible through the smoke in a confusion of helmets, cries, sabres, the heaving rumps of horses, amid the cannon and the trumpet-blast, a disciplined and dreadful tumult with breastplates gleaming like a serpent's scales.

These are tales that seem to belong to another age, legends of centaurs, titans with the heads of men and the bodies of horses galloping to the assault of Olympus, terrible, invulnerable, and sublime, both gods and beasts.

By a strange coincidence the attack of twenty-six squadrons was to be met by the same number of enemy battalions. Behind the ridge of the plateau and in the shadow of the masked battery, Wellington's infantry was formed up in thirteen squares, two battalions in each, the squares being arrayed in two lines of seven and six. Thirteen squares of motionless, resolute men waiting with levelled muskets for what was to come. They could not see their attackers, nor could the attackers see them. They could only hear the rising tide of men, the growing thunder of hooves, the jingle and the clatter of harness, the growl of a savage breath. There was a dreadful silence, and suddenly there appeared on the crest of the ridge a long line of uplifted arms brandishing sabres, helmets, trumpets, grey-moustached faces. With a cry of '*Vive l'empéreur!*' the cavalry, like the coming of an earthquake, swept on to the plateau.

And now a tragedy occurred. On the French right, and the English left, the head of the column of cuirassiers suddenly recoiled in indescribable confusion. Having surmounted the crest of the ridge, and as they broke into the full fury of their charge on the guns and the squares, the horsemen perceived that between themselves and the enemy there was a deep ditch – a grave. It was the sunken lane of Ohain.

What followed was appalling. This ravine, some fifteen feet deep between sheer banks, appeared suddenly at the feet of the leading horses, which reared and attempted to pull up but were thrust forward by those coming behind, so that horse and rider fell and slid helplessly down, to be followed by others. The column had become a projectile, and the explosive force generated for the destruction of the enemy was now its own destroyer. That hideous gulf could only be crossed when it was filled. Horses and men poured into it, pounding each other into a solid mass of flesh, and when the level of the dead and the living had risen high enough the rest of the column passed over. In this fashion a third of Dubois's brigade was lost.

It was the beginning of the defeat.

According to local tradition, which is clearly exaggerated, two thousand horses and fifteen hundred men perished in the sunken lane of Ohain. The figure probably includes bodies which were thrown into it later, on the day after the battle.

Before ordering the charge Napoleon had carefully surveyed the ground, but without seeing the lane, of which nothing was visible above the level of the plateau. But the sight of the white chapel standing at the bend of the Nivelles road had prompted him to put a question to the guide, Lacoste, presumably concerning the possibility of other obstacles. Lacoste had answered in the negative. It can almost be said that the shaking of a peasant's head was the cause of Napoleon's downfall.

But there are other considerations. To the question, was it possible for Napoleon to win this battle, our answer is, No. Because of Wellington? Because of Blücher? No. Because of God.

For Napoleon to have won Waterloo would have been counter to the tide of the nineteenth century. Other events were preparing in which he had no part to play, and their opposition to himself had long been apparent.

It was time for that great man to fall.

His excessive weight in human affairs was upsetting the balance; his huge stature overtopped mankind. That there should be so great a concentration of vitality, so large a world contained within the mind of a single man, must in the end have been fatal to civilization. The time had come for the Supreme Arbiter to decide. Probably a murmur of complaint had come from those principles and elements on which the ordering of all things, moral and material, depends. The reek of blood, the over-filled graveyard, the weeping mother, these are powerful arguments. When the earth is overcharged with suffering, a mysterious lament rising from the shadows is heard in the heights.

Napoleon had been impeached in Heaven and his fall decreed; he was troublesome to God.

Waterloo was not a battle but a change in the direction of the world.

The plateau of Mont-Saint-Jean

Simultaneously with the disclosure of the ravine the guns were unmasked. Sixty cannon and the musket-fire from thirteen squares ravaged the cuirassiers at point-blank range. The intrepid General Delord greeted his enemies with a military salute, and the charge of the cuirassiers continued without a pause. The disaster of the sunken lane had decimated but not dismayed them. They were men of the kind whose hearts grow larger as their numbers shrink.

Only Wathier's column had suffered. Delord's column, which Ney had caused to veer to the left, as though he suspected a trap, was still intact. Galloping *ventre à terre*, reins loose, pistol in hand and sabre between the teeth, the cuirassiers charged the English squares.

There are moments in battle when the souls of men so harden as to turn flesh to stone. Beneath this furious assault the English forces were unshaken. The mêlée was indescribable. The squares were attacked on all sides, ringed round with an inferno of assailants, and stayed immovable. The first row, kneeling, met the horsemen with their bayonets while the second row fired; and behind the second row the gunners of the light artillery reloaded. The ranks parted to allow the discharge of grape-shot and then re-closed. The cuirassiers' answer was to crush them, the huge horses trampling down the men and overleaping the bayonets to plunge gigantically within those living walls. The hail of fire ploughed gaps in the ranks of the cuirassiers and the cuirassiers forced breaches in the squares. The squares shrank in size as their numbers diminished, but they did not break, and they kept up a ceaseless fire against their assailants. The battle assumed a monstrous aspect, with the squares ceasing to be formations of men and becoming craters, the horsemen ceasing to be cavalry and becoming a tempest, every square a volcano enveloped in a thunder-cloud, lava defying the lightning.

The square on the extreme right, the most vulnerable of all being partly isolated, was almost annihilated in the first assault. It consisted of the 75th Highland regiment. Indifferent to the slaughter around him, the regimental piper, seated on a drum, continued to play airs that were the echo of his native forests, lakes, and hills. Those

Scotsmen died remembering Ben Nevis as the Greeks had died remembering Argos – until a sabre-stroke, cutting down both bagpipe and the arm that held it, put an end to the lament.

The cuirassiers, relatively few in numbers and further weakened by the disaster of the sunken lane, were opposed to nearly the whole strength of Wellington's army, but they seemed to multiply, each man to possess the strength of ten. Certain of the Hanoverian battalions showed signs of giving ground, and seeing this Wellington bethought him of his own cavalry. If Napoleon at the same moment had thought of his infantry he would have won the battle. This oversight was his fatal error.

Suddenly the attacking cuirassiers found themselves under a two-fold attack, the infantry squares in front of them and in their rear Somerset with his fourteen hundred dragoons. On his right was Dornberg with the German Light Horse, and on his left Trip with the Belgian heavy cavalry. The cuirassiers were thus attacked on all sides, but they were a whirlwind, their bravery beyond words. Only Englishmen of equal stature could confront Frenchmen such as these.

It was no longer a conflict of men but of shadows, furies, spirits exalted in a tempest of high courage amid the flashing of swords. Within minutes Somerset's fourteen hundred dragoons had been reduced to eight hundred, and Fuller, their lieutenant-colonel, was dead. Ney brought in Lefebvre-Desnouettes with his lancers and *chasseurs*. The Mont-Saint-Jean plateau was taken, re-taken, and taken again. The squares still held, surviving a dozen assaults. Ney had four horses killed under him. Half the cuirassiers were left dead or wounded on the plateau. The struggle lasted two hours.

The English army was profoundly shaken. There can be no doubt that had their first attack not been weakened by the tragedy of the sunken lane the cuirassiers would have broken the centre and gained the day. Clinton, who had seen Talavera and Badajoz, was amazed by that remarkable cavalry, and Wellington, more than half defeated, stoically murmured, 'Splendid!'

The cuirassiers broke seven squares out of the thirteen, captured or spiked sixty guns, and captured six regimental standards which were presented to the Emperor outside the Belle-Alliance farm by a party of three cuirassiers and three *chasseurs* of the Guard.

Wellington's position had decidedly worsened. That battle was like a duel between two grievously wounded men, each with the blood draining out of him, neither willing to yield. The question was, which would be the first to fall?

And still the struggle for the plateau continued. As to exactly how far the cuirassiers penetrated, no one can say, but it is known that the body of a cuirassier, with that of his horse, was found in the toll weighing-shed at the point where the four roads meet – those from Nivelles, Genappe, La Hulpe, and Brussels – having ridden right through the English lines. One of the men who carried the body away is still living at Mont-Saint-Jean, a man named Dehaze who was then eighteen.

Wellington knew that he was near to disaster. In a sense the cuirassiers had failed to achieve their objective, since they had not broken the English centre. Both sides were lodged on the plateau, but neither held it, and in fact the English still occupied the greater part. They had the village and its surrounding land, whereas Ney had only the ridge and its slopes. Both sides seemed to have taken root in that fateful soil.

But the weakness of the English seemed past remedy. Their losses had been appalling. Kempt, on the left wing, cried out for reinforcements, to which Wellington replied that there were none – 'they must fight till they drop'. And at almost the same moment, by a coincidence which illustrates the exhaustion of both armies, Ney was asking Napoleon for infantry and Napoleon was exclaiming: 'Where does he think I can get any? Does he expect me to manufacture them?'

Wellington's case was even worse. His infantry had been so badly mauled by the cuirassiers that in some sectors only a few men grouped round the colours marked the remains of a regiment. Battalions were commanded by captains or lieutenants, and indeed the list of senior officers killed or wounded on both sides was hideously long. Moreover Cumberland's Hanoverian Hussars, a whole regiment under their commander, Colonel Hacke (who was later court-martialled and cashiered), took to their heels and bolted into the forest of Soignes, spreading the news of disaster as far as Brussels. Baggage waggons, ammunition-limbers, carts of wounded, seeing the French gain ground and draw near the forest, followed them; and the Dutch cried havoc. By the account of eye-witnesses still living, the train of fugitives stretched five miles and more in the direction of Brussels. So great was the panic that it reached the Prince de Condé at Malines and Louis XVIII at Ghent. Except for a small reserve stationed behind the field hospital set up in the Mont-Saint-Jean farm, and Vivian's and Vandeleur's brigades on his left wing, Wellington had no more cavalry, and a large number of his guns were out of action. These facts are reported by Siborne, and Pringle, somewhat exaggerating, claims that the Anglo-Dutch strength was reduced to 34,000 men. The Iron Duke remained calm but he was white-lipped. The Austrian and French military attachés, who were with the English headquarters staff, believed that the day was lost. At five o'clock Wellington looked at his watch and was heard to murmur: 'Blücher – or darkness.'

It was at about this moment that a line of bayonets came into view in the distance, twinkling on the heights round Frischemont.

This was the turning-point.

The two guides

Napoleon's tragic miscalculation is known to everyone: he looked for Grouchy but it was Blücher who came – death instead of life. Destiny is shaped by moments such as this: with his eyes upon the throne of the world, he saw the shadow of St Helena.

If the shepherd boy who acted as guide to Bülow, Blücher's second-in-command, had advised him to come by the route above Frischemont, instead of by that below Planchenoit, the pattern of the nineteenth century might well have been different. Napoleon would have won Waterloo. Any other road, except the one below Planchenoit, would have brought the Prussian army to a ravine impassable by artillery, and Bülow would not have arrived in time. According to the Prussian General Muffling, a further hour's delay would have spelt disaster.

There had been much delay already. Bülow had bivouacked at Dion-le-Mont and set out at dawn, but he had been greatly hindered by the state of the road. Moreover, he had had to cross the river Dyle by the narrow bridge at Wavre. The French had set fire to the village street leading to the bridge, and since the ammunition waggons could not pass between the rows of burning houses they had to wait for the fire to be put out. It was not until noon that Bülow's advance-guard reached Chapelle-Saint-Lambert.

Had the battle begun two hours earlier it would have been over by four o'clock, and Blücher, too, would have fallen victim to Napoleon. Such are the immeasurable hazards of a Fatality beyond our grasp.

The Emperor, with his field-glass, was the first to see something on the horizon that fixed his attention. 'A sort of cloud,' he muttered. 'It looks to me like troops.' And turning to the Duke of Dalmatia he said: 'Soult, what can you see around Chapelle-Saint-Lambert?' Using his own glass the marshal replied: 'Four or five thousand men, Sire. It must be Grouchy.' All the glasses of the general staff were turned on this 'cloud', which remained motionless. Some officers thought that it was a halted column of men, but the majority believed it to be a grove of trees. The Emperor sent Domon's contingent of light cavalry to reconnoitre.

The fact is that Bülow had not moved because his advance-guard was weak. His orders were to concentrate his main force before joining battle. But at five o'clock, seeing Wellington's precarious state, Blücher ordered Bülow into the attack with the notable words: 'We must give the English a breather.'

Shortly afterwards, the divisions of Losthin, Hiller, Hacke, and Ryssel deployed ahead of Lobau's corps; Prince William of Prussia's cavalry debouched from the Bois de Paris, Planchenoit was in flames, and artillery fire began to reach as far as the ranks of the Imperial Guard drawn up behind Napoleon.

The Imperial Guard

We know the rest, the intervention of a third army and the transformation of the battle: eighty-six pieces of artillery bursting into sudden thunder, Pirch I overtaking Bülow, Zieten's cavalry led by Blücher in person, the French driven back in disorder under the combined English and Prussian fire as darkness began to fall. Disaster in front and disaster on the flank, and the Guard flung in in an attempt to stay the hideous collapse. Knowing they were about to die, the men shouted, '*Vive l'empéreur!*' History knows no more poignant moment.

The sky had been overcast all day, but at eight o'clock that evening it cleared to allow the sinister red light of the setting sun to flood through the elms of the Nivelles road – the same sun that had risen at Austerlitz.

In this last crisis every battalion was commanded by a general. Friant, Michel, Roguet, Harlet, Porlet de Morvan, all were there. When the tall helmets of the grenadiers, adorned with the eagle badge, emerged from the mist of battle, steadfast, impeccably aligned, magnificent, the enemy felt the splendour of France and for an instant the victors hesitated. But Wellington cried, 'Up Guards and shoot straight!' and the red-coated Englishmen rose from their shelter behind hedges and poured out a withering volley that rent to shreds the tricolour and the eagles. Both sides charged and the last carnage began. The men of the Garde Impériale felt the army giving way around them in the disorder of total rout, the shouts of '*Vive l'empéreur!*' turning to '*sauve qui peut*', and amid disaster on every side they continued to advance forward, dying with every step they took. No man hesitated, no soldier of the line but was the equal of his general in courage, no man flinched from suicide.

Ney, splendid in his acceptance of death, exposed himself to every hazard. He had a fifth horse killed under him. Foaming at the mouth, wild-eyed and running with sweat, his tunic unbuttoned, one epaulette half shorn away by a sabre-stroke and his eagle- badge pierced by a bullet, bleeding and superb with a broken sword in his hand, he cried, 'This is how a Marshal of France dies on the field of battle!' But he did not die. Distraught and furious, he called to Drouet d'Erlon, 'Why haven't you got yourself killed?' And he cried amid the hail of bullets, 'Isn't there one for me? I'd like the whole lot in my belly!'* He was reserved for French bullets, unhappy man.

---

*   These words have been authenticated. Ney was executed on 7 October 1815, having been condemned to death by the French Chamber.

Catastrophe

In the rear of the Guard a grievous confusion prevailed.

The army was hastily falling back at every point – from Hougomont, La-Haie-Sainte, Papelotte, Planchenoit. The cry of treason was mingled with the cry of *sauve qui peut*. A disintegrating army is like the thawing of a glacier, a mindless, jostling commotion, total disruption. Ney found himself another horse and hatless and weaponless sought to make a stand on the Brussels road, striving to hold up both the English and the flying French, who swept past him crying '*Vive le maréchal Ney*' as they fled. He showered them with appeals and insults but was overborne. Two of Durutte's regiments were weaving this way and that, rebounding like shuttlecocks between the sabres of the Uhlans and the muskets of Wellington's infantry. Rout is the most hideous of all mêlées, with friends striking each other down in the effort to escape, formations losing all coherence and becoming the scattered foam of battle. Lobau on one wing and Reille on the other, both were swept away by that tide. Napoleon made vain efforts to set up a barrier with the last of the Guard and the commissariat detachments. Galloping along the lines of fleeing men he, too, besought, urged, threatened. It was all in vain. The gunners, unharnessing the horses from the guns, were using them to get away. Overturned guns and supply-waggons blocked the crowded roads, adding to the slaughter. The Prussian cavalry, newly arrived and unwearied, played havoc with the panic-stricken horde of men who, casting aside their weapons and ignoring their officers, sought to escape by way of roads, footpaths, bridges, fields, hills, and villages. An army of 40,000 men, the lions of France, become sheep for Zieten to slaughter at his leisure. That was the picture.

A last attempt at a stand was made at Genappe, where Lobau succeeded in rallying three hundred men. The entrance to the village was barricaded, but at the first blast of Prussian grape-shot, traces of which are still to be seen on the brickwork of a ruined building outside the village, the flight was resumed. It became atrocious. Blücher ordered that no man was to be spared, and Roguet set an example by announcing that he would shoot every grenadier who had taken a Prussian prisoner. Duhesme, the general commanding the Young Guard, caught in the doorway of a Genappe tavern, offered his sword to a Death's Head hussar in token of surrender; the hussar took it and then killed him. To the dishonour of old Blücher, victory was crowned with murder – let us punish, for we are history! The rout swept through Genappe, Quatre-Bras, Gosselies, Frasnes, Charleroi, Thuin, and did not stop till it reached the frontier – and this rabble of desperate men was the Grande Armée!

But was there no cause for this total collapse of an army whose gallantry had astonished the world? Yes. The shadow of a momentous justice lay over Waterloo. It was the day of destiny, when a force greater than mankind prevailed. Hence the terrified bowing of heads, the surrender of so many noble spirits. The conquerors of Europe were stricken with helplessness, unable to say or do anything as they felt the weight of that terrible Presence. *Hoc erat in fatis* – so was it written! On that day the course of mankind was altered.

Waterloo was the hinge of the nineteenth century. A great man had to disappear in order that a great century might be born. One who is Unanswerable had taken the matter in hand, and thus the panic of so many heroes is explained. It was not merely a shadow that fell upon Waterloo but a thunderbolt; it was God himself.

At nightfall, in a field near Genappe, two officers, Bernard and Bertrand, came up with a haggard-eyed man who, having been borne thus far by the tide of defeat, had dismounted and, holding his horse by the bridle, was walking back alone in the direction of Waterloo. It was Napoleon, still trying to go forward, the giant somnambulist of a shattered dream.

The last square

A few squares of the French guards, as immobile in the rout as rocks in a torrent of water held out until nightfall. The coming of night meant the coming of death, and they waited unshakably for that double darkness to engulf them. Each individual regiment, sundered from the others and having no link with the army as a whole, died in its own way. They had taken up their last positions, some on the uplands of Rossomme, others on the plateau of Mont-Saint-Jean; here, abandoned but still formidable, they suffered their final agony, and Ulm, Wagram, Jena, and Friedland died with them.

By nine o'clock that evening only one square, at the foot of the plateau of the Mont-Saint-Jean, the slope scored by the hooves of the cuirassiers, was holding out against the concentrated artillery-fire of the victorious enemy. It was commanded by a little-known officer named Cambronne. With every burst of fire the square diminished but still it fought back, answering salvoes with rifle-fire, tightening its shrunken walls, while the fleeing men from other units, pausing to take breath, listened to the dwindling thunders of the battle amid the gathering night.

When finally only a handful of men was left, the heaped dead more numerous than the living, the flag in tatters, the ammunition-less muskets become no more than cudgels, a kind of superstitious awe assailed the victors and the English guns held their fire. There was a momentary pause. Those last defenders saw as though it were a gathering of spectres the dark figures of their enemy closing in on them, men on horseback and guns outlined against the fading pallor of the sky, and over all the giant death's-head which is the ghost that haunts all battlefields. They could hear the sound of the guns being reloaded and see the lighted fuses gleaming like the eyes of tigers in the dusk. In this final moment, when all was in suspense, one of the English generals, Colville or Maitland, called out to them, 'Brave Frenchmen, will you not surrender?' Cambronne answered, '*Merde!*'

Cambronne

From respect for the decencies of language this word, perhaps the greatest ever uttered by a Frenchman, is not repeated in the history books; the sublime is banned from the record. At our risk and peril we have defied the ban. Amid the giants of that day there was one greater than all others, and it was Cambronne.

To speak the word and die, what can be greater than this? To accept death is to die, and it was not the fault of the man if, wounded, he nevertheless survived. The real victor of Waterloo was not the defeated Napoleon, or Wellington, who was so nearly defeated, or Blücher, who scarcely fought; it was Cambronne. Thus to defy the lightnings is to be victorious.

To meet disaster in this fashion, challenging Fate itself, setting a springboard for the lion resurgent, hurling into the rainswept darkness that obscene retort that mocked the traitorous wall of Hougomont, the sunken lane of Ohain, the failure of Grouchy, the coming of Blücher; to incarnate irony at the mouth of the grave, staying erect when prostrate; to demolish the European coalition with a word, fling in the face of kings the *cloaca* known to the Caesars, make the crudest of words into the greatest by investing it with the splendour of France, insolently conclude Waterloo with *mardi-gras*, complete Leonidas with Rabelais, compress this victory in a single word that may not be spoken, losing the field but gaining history and at the end of carnage winning to one's side the hosts of laughter – this is sublime.

There they were, the kings of Europe, the triumphant generals, those thundering Jupiters, with a hundred thousand men and a million more behind them, with the gaping guns and the lighted fuses. They had trampled down the Imperial Guard and the Grande Armée; they had set their foot on Napoleon; and now there was only Cambronne, the earthworm who still outfaced them, searching for a word as one may reach for a sword. The word was spat out of his mouth. He hurled his scorn at that prodigious, mediocre victory, that victory without victors, feeling its impact but knowing its hollowness. He did more than spit: borne down by the weight of numbers and material circumstance, he expressed in a word the spirit that transcends those things, and the word meant excrement. Let us repeat it, to do this was to conquer.

The spirit of the greatest days visited that unknown man at that fateful moment. He found the word for Waterloo as Rouget de l'Isle had found the 'Marseillaise', in a breath of inspiration. The living breath passed through the ranks and the men shuddered and sang or uttered their death-cry. Cambronne's expression of giant contempt was hurled not merely at Europe in the name of the Empire, which would have been little enough: it was hurled at the past in the name of the Revolution; it was Danton speaking, Kléber bellowing defiance.

At the word an English voice gave the order to fire and the batteries flamed in a last, terrible belching of grape-shot. The hillside trembled. For a time the scene was obscured by a dense cloud of smoke touched here and there by the rays of the rising moon, and when this drifted away it could be seen that there was nothing left. That formidable remnant had been annihilated. The four walls of the living fortress lay shattered on the ground, with only here and there a movement among the bodies of the dead. Thus did the legions of France, greater than the legions of Rome, expire on the rain-soaked, blood-soaked earth of the Mont-Saint-Jean, amid the darkened corn, at the place where now the post-cart passes at four in the morning on its way to Nivelles, with Joseph the postman blithely whipping up his horse.

Quot libras in duce[*]

The Battle of Waterloo is an enigma as incomprehensible to the winners as to the loser. To Napoleon it was a panic; Blücher saw it simply as a matter of fire-power, and Wellington did not understand it at all. We have only to study the accounts, the confused reports, the contradictory views. The French General, Jomini, distinguishes four crucial moments; the German, Muffling, divides it into three stages. Lieutenant-Colonel Charras, whose views we do not always share, is alone in discerning the true nature of that collapse of the human intelligence at odds with divine hazard. All other historians are in some degree bewildered by it and grope in their bewilderment. It was a momentous day indeed, the collapse of a militarist monarchy which, to the amazement of kings, involved every kingdom in the overthrow of armed force and the defeat of war.

In an event of this nature, bearing the stamp of more than human necessity, the part played by man is negligible.

If we deny to Wellington and Blücher all credit for the victory of Waterloo, do we in any way detract from the greatness of England and Germany? No. The greatness of those countries is in no way affected by the happening at Waterloo. Peoples are great, thank Heaven, irrespective of the grim chances of the sword. Neither England nor Germany nor France can be contained in a scabbard. Overshadowing

---

[*]   Taken from the tenth Satire of Juvenal, referring specifically to Hannibal. Lit. 'How much does the General weigh?'

Blücher, in that epoch when Waterloo was no more than a clashing of sabres, was the Germany of Goethe, and over-shadowing Wellington was the England of Byron. A huge upsurging of ideas is the keynote of our century, and England and Germany each lends its own splendour to the light of the new dawn. They are illustrious because they think. The ennoblement which they bring to civilization is their own quality, born of themselves, not of any accident. Their increased greatness in the nineteenth century is not due to Waterloo. Only barbarian peoples are suddenly enhanced by victory, like streams swollen by a sudden downpour. Civilized peoples, particularly in our present age, neither rise nor sink according to the good or ill-fortune of a military leader. Their specific gravity in the human race is the result of something more than conflict. Their honour, thank God, their dignity, their genius and the light they shed, are not merely numbers drawn in the lottery of battle by those gamblers, the heroes and conquerors. Often the losing of a battle leads to the winning of progress. Less glory but greater liberty: the drum is silent and the voice of reason can be heard. It is a game of 'loser wins'. We must view Waterloo coolly in either aspect, rendering unto Chance what belongs to Chance and to God what belongs to God. It was not in the true sense a victory. It was a lucky throw of the dice.

A throw of the dice won by Europe and paid for by France – scarcely worth erecting the effigy of a lion to mark the spot.

It was the strangest encounter in history. Napoleon and Wellington were not enemies but opposites. Never has God, who delights in antitheses, contrived a more striking contrast or a more extraordinary confrontation. On the one side precision, foresight, shrewd calculation, cool tenacity, and military correctitude; reserves husbanded, the way of retreat ensured, advantage taken of the terrain; warfare ordered by the book with nothing left to chance. On the other side intuition, divination, military unorthodoxy, more than human instinct, the eye of the eagle that strikes with lightning swiftness, prodigious art mingled with reckless impetuosity; all the mysteries of an unfathomable nature, the sense of kinship with Destiny; river, plain, forest, and hill summoned and in some sort forced into compliance; the despot tyrannizing over the battlefield, faith in a star mingled with military science, enriching but also undermining it. Wellington was the technician of war, Napoleon was its Michelangelo; and this time genius was vanquished by rule-of-thumb.

Each side was awaiting someone, and it was the technician who calculated rightly. Napoleon awaited Grouchy, who did not come; Wellington awaited Blücher, who came.

Wellington represented the revenge of classic warfare. Napoleon in his dawn had met it in Italy and superbly beaten it. The old owl had fled the young hawk; the traditional concept had been not merely shattered but outraged. Who was this twenty-six-year-old Corsican, this magnificent ignoramus, who with everything against him and nothing for him, lacking supplies, munitions, guns, boots, almost lacking an army, had with a handful of men assailed the coalition of Europe and absurdly won impossible victories? Where did he spring from, this whirlwind madman who, without pausing for breath, with only the one force at his

command, pulverized one after another the five armies of
the Austrian Emperor, flinging Beaulieu back on Alvinzi,
Wurmser on Beaulieu, Mélas on Wurmser, and Mack on
Mélas. What was he, this upstart of war with the effrontery
of a thunderbolt? The academic school of warfare disowned
him while falling back before him. Out of this arose an
implacable hatred of the old Caesarism for the new, of
the orthodox sabre for the flaming sword, and of the
conventional strategist for the genius. And on 18 June 1815,
this hatred spoke the last word, inscribing above Lodi,
Montebello, Montenotte, Mantua, Marengo, and Arcola
the name of Waterloo. A triumph of mediocrity pleasing
to the majority. Destiny permitted the irony. Napoleon
in his decline encountered a youthful Wurmser: for to
have another Wurmser we need only whiten Wellington's
hair.

Waterloo was a battle of the first importance won by a
commander of the second rank. What was most impressive
in that battle was England – English steadfastness and reso-
lution, English blood; and what was most superb in England
was, with all respect, herself – not her commander but her
men. Wellington, oddly ungrateful, declared in a letter to
Lord Bathurst that his army – the army that fought on
18 June 1815 – was 'detestable'. What do the bones moulder-
ing in the soil of Waterloo think of that?

England has been too modest in respect of Wellington;
in overloading him with greatness she diminishes herself.
He was heroic, but so were the men he commanded. He was
tenacious – it was his signal quality, and we do not decry
it – but the least of his foot-soldiers and horsemen was as

solid as himself. The iron soldier was the equal of the Iron Duke. And for our part our praises go to the army and the people of England. If any trophy is to be awarded it should go to them. The Waterloo Column in London would do greater justice if it raised to the heavens not the figure of a man but the image of a race.

But these words will not please the English. Despite their revolution of 1688, and our own of 1789, they still cherish their feudal illusions. They believe in heredity and hierarchy. They are a people unsurpassed in power and glory, but they still think of themselves as a nation, not as people. As people they willingly subordinate themselves, accepting a lord as a leader. The workman lets himself be despised, the soldier lets himself be flogged. We may recall that after the Battle of Inkerman a sergeant who had, it seems, saved the army could not be mentioned in dispatches by Lord Raglan because the English military hierarchy does not allow any man of less than commissioned rank to be named in a report.

What is wonderful in all battles on the scale of Waterloo is the part played in them by chance. The rain-sodden field, the sunken lane, the deafness of Grouchy, the guide who misled Napoleon and the guide who led Blücher aright – chance was marvellously skilful in its ordering of that débâcle.

It may be added that Waterloo was more a massacre than a battle. Of all set battles it was fought on the narrowest front in relation to the numbers of troops engaged. Napoleon's front was about three miles, Wellington's about two, and there were some 72,000 men on either side – hence the carnage. It has been estimated that at Austerlitz the French losses amounted to 14 per cent, the Russian to 30 per cent, and the Austrian to 44 per cent; and that at Wagram the French lost 13 per cent and the Austrians 14 per cent. At Waterloo the French losses were 56 per cent and the Allied losses 31 per cent, making a total for both armies of 41 per cent; 145,000 combatants, 60,000 dead.

The field of Waterloo today resembles any other stretch of country; it has the stillness of the earth which is the impassive nourisher of man. But at night a sort of visionary mist arises from it, and the traveller who chooses to look and listen, dreaming like Virgil on the field of Philippi, may catch the echoes of catastrophe. That monumental hillock with its nondescript lion vanishes, and the fearful event comes back to life. The battlefield recovers its reality, the lines of infantry wavering across the plain, the furious charges, the gleam of sabres and bayonets, the flame and thunder of cannon-fire. Like a groan emerging from the depths of a tomb the listener may hear the clamour of a ghostly conflict and see the shadowy forms of grenadiers and cuirassiers and the images of men departed – here Napoleon, there Wellington. All gone but still locked in combat, while the ditches run with blood, the trees shudder, the sound of fury rises to the sky and over those windblown heights – Mont-Saint-Jean, Hougomont, Frischemont, Papelotte, Planchenoit – the spectral armies whirl in mutual extermination.

Should we approve of Waterloo?

There exists a highly respectable school of liberal thought which does not deplore Waterloo. We are not of their number. To us Waterloo is the date of the confounding of liberty. It is strange that such a bird should have been hatched out of such an egg.

Waterloo, in terms of its ultimate significance, is the considered triumph of counter-revolution. It is Europe versus France, St Petersburg, Berlin, and Vienna versus Paris, the *status quo* versus the new order, the 15th of July 1789 attacked by way of the 20th of March 1815, the move to action-stations of monarchy against the indomitable upheaval of the French people. To subdue that great people which had been in a state of eruption for twenty-six years, such was its aim, an affirmation of solidarity between the Houses of Brunswick, Nassau, Romanoff, Hohenzollern, and Hapsburg, and the House of Bourbon. Waterloo was the assertion of the Divine Right of Kings. It is true that since the Empire had been a despotism, royalty was forced by a natural reaction to answer it with a degree of liberalism, and that a grudging constitutionalism emerged from Waterloo, to the great displeasure of the victors. The fact is that the Revolution, being wholly inevitable, could not be really destroyed. It re-emerged before Waterloo in the form of Bonaparte overthrowing old thrones, and after Waterloo in the person of Louis XVIII volunteering and submitting to the Charter. Bonaparte set an innkeeper's son on the throne of Naples and an ex-sergeant on the Swedish throne, proclaiming equality by the practice of inequality; Louis XVIII at Saint-Ouen endorsed the Declaration of the Rights of Man. To understand the nature of the Revolution we must call it 'progress'; and we may define progress by the word 'tomorrow'. Tomorrow irresistibly does its work, yesterday as today, and it always achieves its aims, although by strange means. It caused Wellington to make Foy, a plain soldier, into an orator: he fell wounded at Hougomont to re-emerge in parliament. That is the method of Progress, the craftsman to whom all tools are serviceable, the man who bestrode the Alps and the old, sick, well-intentioned monarch Louis XVIII, the conqueror and the gout invalid, one for use outside France, the other within. Waterloo put an end to the overthrow of European thrones by the sword, but the effect of this was to cause the work of revolution to proceed in another form. The day of the swordsmen was ended, the thinkers took their place. The tides of the century which Waterloo sought to stem flowed over the battle-field and still rose; that sinister victory was defeated by liberty.

To sum up, it is beyond question that the victor at Waterloo, the power behind Wellington which brought to his aid every field-marshal's baton in Europe (including, it is said, that of the Maréchal de France), which inspired the building of that mound of earth and bones on which was set the lion triumphant, which urged Blücher on to sabre the fleeing army, and which from the plateau of Mont-Saint-Jean hung over France like a bird of prey, this power was the counter-revolution. This was the power that murmured the infamous word 'dismemberment': but then, arrived at Paris, seeing the crater at its feet and realizing its peril, counter-revolution hastily revised its views and fell back upon babble about a charter.

We must read into Waterloo no more than it truly represented. There was no intention of liberty. The counter-revolution involuntarily turned liberal just as Napoleon, by a parallel phenomenon, involuntarily turned revolutionary. On 18 June 1815, that Robespierre-on-horseback was unseated.

Revival of divine right

Dictatorship was ended, and with it a European system collapsed.

The Napoleonic empire dissolved in a darkness resembling the last days of Rome, and chaos loomed as in the time of the barbarians. But the barbarism of 1815, which must be called by its proper name of counter-revolution, was short-winded and soon stopped for lack of breath. The Empire, be it said, was mourned; tears were shed for it by heroic eyes. If glory be the sword turned sceptre, then the Empire was the embodiment of glory. It had diffused all the light that tyranny can shed, a sombre light, and worse, an obscure light which, compared with the true light of day, is darkness; and the ending of this darkness was like the ending of an eclipse.

Louis XVIII returned to Paris, and the dancing in the streets on 8 July effaced the enthusiasm of 20 March. The exile was back on the throne, a white banner flew from the Tuileries and the pinewood table from Hartwell was placed in front of the fleur-de-lis-embroidered chair of Louis XIV. Bouvines and Fontenoy were the happenings of yesterday, while Austerlitz had faded from sight. Altar and throne majestically clasped hands, and one of the least contested forms of nineteenth-century social health became established in France and throughout the Continent. Europe adopted the white cockade. The device *non pluribus impar*, 'not least among the many', reappeared in the stone sunburst decorating the barracks on the Quai d'Orsay. The Arc du Carrousel, with its tale of ill-famed victories, uncomfortable amid so much novelty and perhaps a little ashamed of Marengo and Arcola, saved its face with a statue of the Duc d'Angoulême. The cemetery of the Madeleine, the public graveyard in 1793, was covered over with marble and jasper, since within its dust lay the bones of Louis XVI and Marie Antoinette. A funeral monument rose amid the ramparts of Vincennes to commemorate the fact that the Duc d'Enghien had died in the month in which Napoleon had been crowned. Pope Pius VII, who had performed the ceremony, blessed the downfall as serenely as he had blessed the coronation. In the Palace of Schönbrunn, outside Vienna, there lingered the shadowy figure of a four-year-old boy whom it was seditious to refer to as the King of Rome. And all this happened – the kings returned to their thrones, the master of Europe was caged, the *ancien régime* became the new régime, and all the darkness and light in the world changed places – because on a summer afternoon a shepherd had said to a Prussian general in a wood, 'Go this way and not that way.'

That autumn of 1815 was like a melancholy spring. Old, poisonous realities changed their outward appearance, lies were wedded to the year 1789, divine right hid behind a charter, fictions became legal truths, prejudice, super-stition, and moral dishonesty, taking Article 14 to heart, acquired the gloss of liberalism, all snakes sloughed their skins.

The stature of mankind had been at once heightened and diminished by Napoleon. The ideal, in that reign of splendid materialism, was given the strange name of ideology, a grave miscalculation on the part of the great man, making a mock of the future. But the people, that cannon-fodder that so loved the gunner, sought him everywhere. Where was he and what was he doing? 'Napoleon is dead,' a man shouted to a crippled survivor of Marengo and Waterloo . . . 'Him dead!' the soldier shouted back. 'That's how well you know him!' Imagination deified the fallen despot and for a long time after Waterloo the heart of Europe was overcast in the enormous emptiness left by his passing.

The kings took it upon themselves to fill this vacuum, and Europe used it for its own re-shaping. The *Belle Alliance* before Waterloo became the Holy Alliance.

Confronted by this reorganization of ancient Europe, the outlines of a new France began to emerge. The future which the Emperor had mocked made its appearance, bearing on its forehead the star of Liberty. Young eyes looked ardently towards it, but, a strange paradox, they were in love both with the future, which was Liberty, and with the past, which was Napoleon. The defeated gained stature in defeat and Bonaparte fallen appeared greater than Napoleon erect. England placed him in the charge of Hudston Lowe and France appointed Montchenu to keep an eye on him. His folded arms were the terror of thrones, and Alexander called him, 'My sleepless nights.' This fear was due to the force of revolution that was in him, and it explains and justifies Bonapartist liberalism. The exiled spirit still shook the old world and the kings reigned uneasily, seeing the rock of St Helena on the skyline.

That was Waterloo.

But in the eye of eternity what did it amount to? Tempest and thunder-cloud, the war and then the peace, not all that turmoil could for an instant trouble the gaze of the immense all-seeing eye wherein a grasshopper jumping from one blade of grass to the next equals the flight of an eagle between the towers of Notre-Dame.

The battlefield at night

Our story requires us to return to the battlefield.

The 18th of June 1815 was a night of full moon. The light favoured Blücher's savage pursuit of the routed army, disclosing the paths of its flight, putting the demoralized troops at the mercy of the ferocious Prussian cavalry and assisting the massacre; thus does night sometimes lend its countenance to disaster.

With the firing of the last shot the plain of Mont-Saint-Jean became deserted. The English moved into the French encampments, it being by custom an assertion of victory to sleep in the bed of the defeated. They set up their bivouacs beyond Rossomme. The Prussians careered onward on the heels of the retreat. Wellington sat down in the village of Waterloo to write his report to Lord Bathurst.

Never has the Virgilian *sic vos non vobis** been more applicable than it is to that village of Waterloo, which was a couple of miles distant from the scene of operations. Mont-Saint-Jean was bombarded; Hougomont, Papelotte, and Planchenoit were set afire; La-Haie-Sainte was carried by assault and La-Belle-Alliance was the meeting place of the victorious armies. Those names are scarcely remembered, whereas Waterloo, which played no part in the battle, has reaped all the glory.

We are not among those who sing the praises of war; we tell the truth about it when the need arises. War has tragic splendours which we have not sought to conceal, but it also has its especial squalors, among which is the prompt stripping of the bodies of the dead. The day following a battle always dawns on naked corpses.

Who are the despoilers, the tarnishers of victory, the furtive hands ransacking the pockets of glory? Certain philosophers, Voltaire among them, maintain that they are precisely the men who created the glory. The same men. The living rob the fallen; the hero of the day becomes the scavenger of the night; and surely he is entitled to do so, since he is responsible for the corpse he robs.

For our part, we do not believe it. We find it inconceivable that the same hands can gather laurels and drag the boots off the feet of the dead. True though it is that the victor is normally followed by the ghoul, we acquit the soldier, and especially the present-day, soldier, of this charge.

---

* *Sic vos non vobis mellificatis apes* – thus do you make honey, but not for yourselves, O bees.

Every army has its camp-followers and it is to these that
we must look, to the bat-like creatures, half-ruffian,
half-servant, engendered by the twilight of war, wearers of
uniform who do no fighting, malingerers, venomous crip-
ples, sutlers riding in small carts, sometimes with their
women, who steal what later they sell, beggars offering their
services as guides, rogues and vagabonds of all kinds. These
were what every army in the past – we do not speak of the
present day – dragged in its train. No army and no country
owned them; they spoke Italian and followed the Germans,
or French and followed the English. Looting was born of
looting. The abominable maxim 'live on the enemy' fostered
the disease, which only strict discipline could quell. Certain
military reputations are misleading; there are generals, even
great ones, whose popularity it is not easy to account for.
Turenne was adored by his men because he tolerated looting; evil condoned wears the mask of benevolence. The
number of pillagers following in the wake of an army varied
according to the severity of the commander. Hoche and
Marceau had none; Wellington – we gladly do him that
justice – had very few.

Nevertheless, the bodies of the dead were robbed during
that night of 18–19 June. Wellington was uncompromising:
any person caught in the act was to be shot forthwith. The
looters preyed on one end of the battlefield while they were
being executed at the other.

The moon shed a sinister light over the plain.

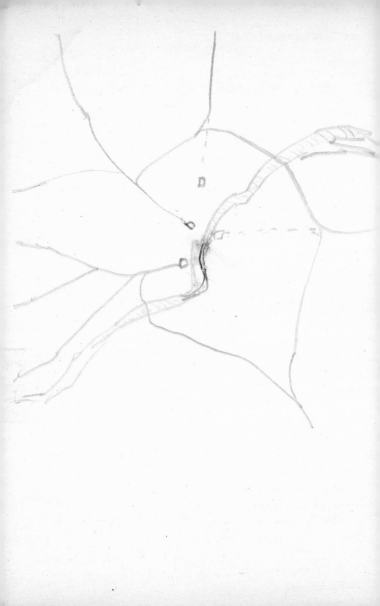